New Practice in Music Theory

by Josephine Koh

Grade 5

Based on the new theory syllabus
of the Associated Board of the
Royal Schools of Music.

Published by
Music Plaza Pte Ltd
No. 11 Ubi Road 1 #06-02
Meiban Industrial Building Singapore 408723

Copyright 1991 © by Music Plaza Pte Ltd
ISBN 981-3012-72-2
2nd Edition 1995
Reprinted 1996
Reprinted 1997
Reprinted 2000
Reprinted 2001
Reprinted 2002

Cover design by Lee Kowling

for Wholesales Enquiries, please write to:
MUSIC PLAZA PTE LTD
No. 11 Ubi Road 1, #06-02
Meiban Industrial Building
Singapore 408723.
ATTN: DORA LIM
TEL: 65-67409308 FAX: 65-67417027

Contents

Irregular Time Signatures

A bar in irregular time is one which cannot be divided into equal groups of two or three beats.

The irregular times to be known in this grade are   (i) Quintuple time and   (ii) Septuple time.

Quintuple Time

There are 5 beats in every bar.

The grouping in quintuple time is (2 + 3) or (3 + 2) beats in a bar.

e.g.

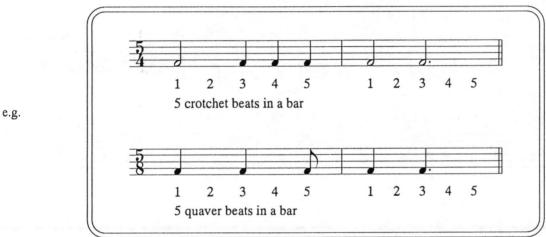

Septuple Time

There are 7 beats per bar.

The grouping in septuple time may be (2 + 2 + 3), (4 + 3), (2 + 3 + 2) or (3 + 2 + 2) beats in a bar.

e.g.

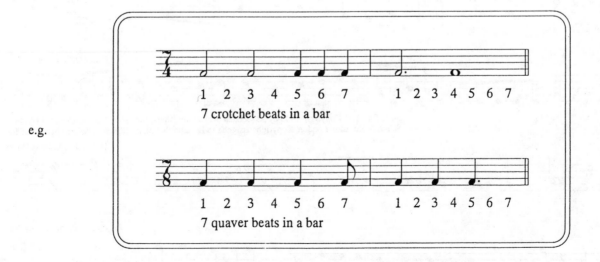

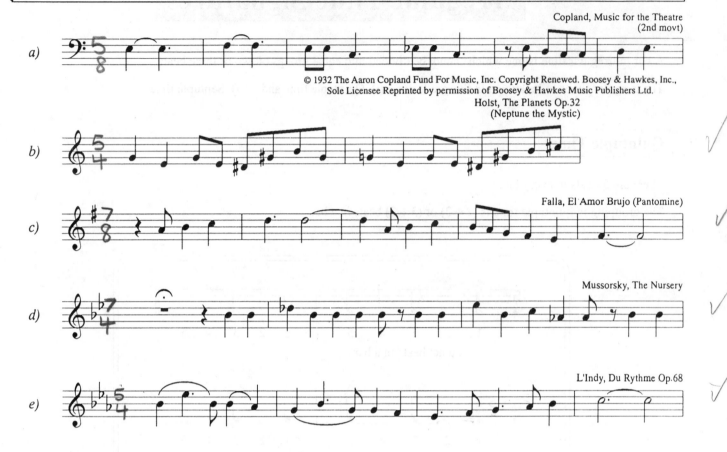

Copland, Music for the Theatre
(2nd movt)

a)

© 1932 The Aaron Copland Fund For Music, Inc. Copyright Renewed. Boosey & Hawkes, Inc.,
Sole Licensee Reprinted by permission of Boosey & Hawkes Music Publishers Ltd.

Holst, The Planets Op.32
(Neptune the Mystic)

b)

Falla, El Amor Brujo (Pantomine)

c)

Mussorsky, The Nursery

d)

L'Indy, Du Rythme Op.68

e)

Holst, The Planets (1st movt)

a)

Lekeu, Sonata in G for Viola
and Piano

b)

Hindemith, Ludus Tonalis

c)

Ludus Tonalis © Copyright 1943 by Associated Music Publishers, Inc., New York. © Copyright 1943 by
Schott & Co. Ltd., London. Copyright assigned to B. Schott's Sohne 1968. Reproduced by permission.

Holst, The Planets (Mars)

d)

Prokofiev, Piano Sonata No.7

e)

© Copyright 1943 by Boosey & Hawkes Music Publishers Ltd.
For the UK, British Commonwealth (excluding Canada), Eire
and South Africa. Reprinted by permission of Boosey
& Hawkes Music Publishers Ltd.

3. The following passages begin on the first beat of the bar. However the time signatures change frequently. Add the time signatures where appropriate.

a) Bernstein, Jeremiah Symphony (3rd movt)

Reprinted by permission of Boosey & Hawkes Music Publishers Ltd.

b) Copland, Concerto for Orchestra and Piano (1st movt)

© 1929 The Aaron Copland Fund For Music, Inc. Copyright Renewed. Boosey & Hawkes, Inc.,
Sole Licensee Reprinted by permission of Boosey & Hawkes Music Publishers Ltd.

c) Ireland, Sonata in G minor for Cello and Piano (1st movt)

© Reproduced by permission of Stainer & Bell Ltd, London, England.

d) Bernstein, Fancy Free Ballet Variation 2

Reprinted by permission of Boosey & Hawkes Music Publishers Ltd.

e) Schumann, Symphony for Strings

f) Stravinsky, Rite of Spring (Mysterious Circles of the Adolescents)

© 1912, 1921 by Hawkes & Son (London) Ltd. Reprinted by permission of Boosey & Hawkes Music Publishers Ltd.

g) Walton, Concerto for Violin and Orchestra (3rd movt)

© 1945 Oxford University Press.

h) Kudosa-Pillanat Kepek, Snapshots Op.69

i) Copland, Duo for Flute and Piano

© 1971 by The Aaron Copland Fund for Music, Inc. Boosey & Hawkes, Inc., Sole Licensee
Reprinted by permission of Boosey & Hawkes Music Publishers Ltd.

j) Stravinsky, Rite of Spring

© 1912, 1921 by Hawkes & Son (London) Ltd. Reprinted by permission of Boosey & Hawkes Music Publishers Ltd.

3

Irregular Time Divisions

Irregular divisions of a beat include **triplets** (in simple time) and **duplets** (in compound time).

A note can also be subdivided into irregular groups.

For example:

The principles of the subdivisions are such that:

(i)   A group of 5, 6 or 7 notes is played in the time of *a group of 4 of the same kind*.

Thus:

(ii) A group of 9 notes is played in the time of *a group of 8 of the same kind*.

Thus:

---

1.   Write a note to represent the time value of each of the following groups.

a)   =   (whole note)

b)   =   (half note)

c)   =   (quarter note)

d)   =   (eighth note)

e)   =   (eighth note)

f)   =   (half note)

g)   =   (half note)

h)   =   (quarter note)

i)   =   (quarter note)

j)   =   (whole note)

k)   =   (quarter note)

l)   =   (eighth note)

2. Add bar-lines to each of the following which begins on the first beat of the bar, unless indicated.

Brahms, Quintet in G Op.111 (2nd movt)

Ireland, Trio No.3 in E minor (3rd movt)

© Copyright 1938 by Hawkes & Son (London) Ltd

Ravel, Tzigane for Violin and Orchestra

Schumann, Carnaval (Eusebius)

Paganini, Concerto No.1 in D Op. 6

Sibelius, Symphony No.1 (2nd movt)

© Breitkopf & Hartel, Weisbaden.

Tchaikovsky, Symphony No. 5

Sibelius, Karelius Op.11

© Breitkopf & Hartel, Weisbaden.

Sibelius, Symphony No.4 (4th movt)

© Breitkopf & Hartel, Weisbaden.

Walton, Concerto for Violin and Orchestra (2nd movt)

© 1945 Oxford University Press.

5

Tenor Clef

The tenor clef  is one of the C clefs. The middle C lies on the 4th line.

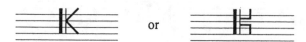

Middle C

It can also be written as:

or

Do not confuse the alto and tenor clefs.

Tenor Clef   Alto Clef

The key signatures of up to 5 sharps and flats are arranged thus:

The tenor clef is used by the cello, bassoon and tenor trombone.

---

1.   Write the letter names of these notes.

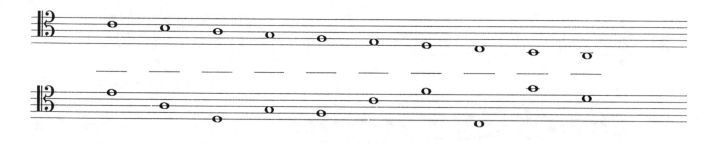

---

2.   Write letter names of each of the notes below, then rewrite them at the same pitch in the other clefs.

E.g.

A flat

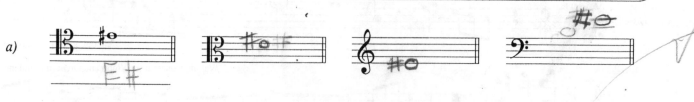

a)

E#

b)

G

6

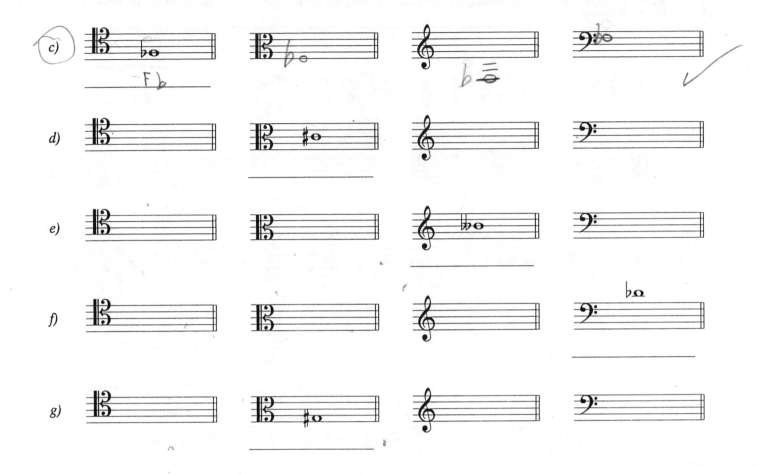

c)   F♭

2. Using the tenor clef, write the required triad of each of the following keys. Use the correct key signature.

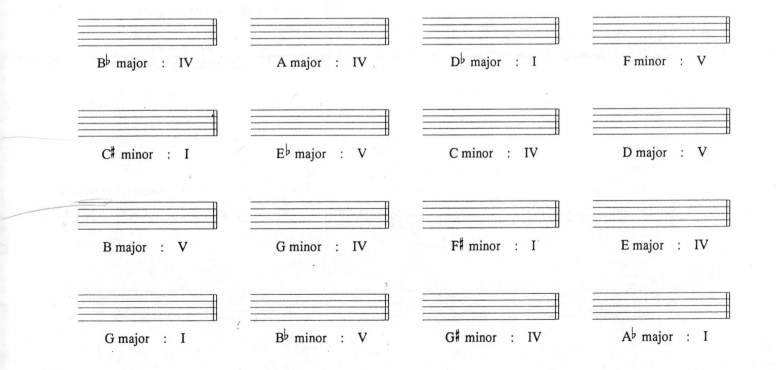

B♭ major : IV	A major : IV	D♭ major : I	F minor : V
C♯ minor : I	E♭ major : V	C minor : IV	D major : V
B major : V	G minor : IV	F♯ minor : I	E major : IV
G major : I	B♭ minor : V	G♯ minor : IV	A♭ major : I

3. Rewrite each of these passages using the tenor clef, keeping the same pitch. (The opening of the first exercise has been shown.)

Grieg, The Lonely Wanderer Op.43 No.2

Debussy, La Mer

Franck, 3 Chorals No.1

Richard Strauss, Till Eulenspiegels

Mozart, Symphony in G minor K550

4. Rewrite these passages at the same pitch in the clefs required.

Major and Minor Keys

In Grade 5, major and minor keys of up to six sharps and flats are to be known.
These keys thus complete the table:

Major key	Key-signature	Minor key
C	–	A
G	F♯	E
D	F♯ C♯	B
A	F♯ C♯ G♯	F♯
E	F♯ C♯ G♯ D♯	C♯
B	F♯ C♯ G♯ D♯ A♯	G♯
F♯	F♯ C♯ G♯ D♯ A♯ E♯	D♯
F	B♭	D
B♭	B♭ E♭	G
E♭	B♭ E♭ A♭	C
A♭	B♭ E♭ A♭ D♭	F
D♭	B♭ E♭ A♭ D♭ G♭	B♭
G♭	B♭ E♭ A♭ D♭ G♭ C♭	E♭

The key signatures with six sharps and flats are written thus:

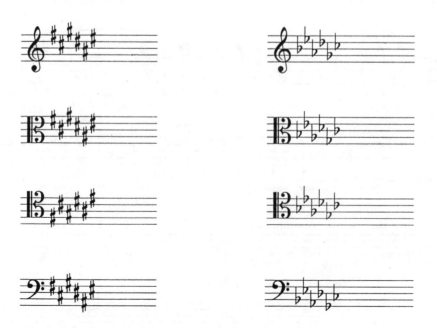

10

1. Add accidentals where necessary to form the scales named. Do not use key signature.

a) E♭ melodic minor

b) F♯ major

c) D♯ harmonic minor

d) G♭ major

e) E♭ harmonic minor

2. Using the correct key signature and adding any necessary accidentals, write the following scales.
Use semibreves only.

a) D♯ melodic minor, descending

b) G♭ major, descending

c) F♯ major, ascending

d) E♭ harmonic minor, descending

e) D♯ harmonic minor, ascending

f) E♭ melodic minor, ascending

3. After the clefs, write triads as indicated in the given keys. Do not use key signatures but add any necessary accidentals before the notes.

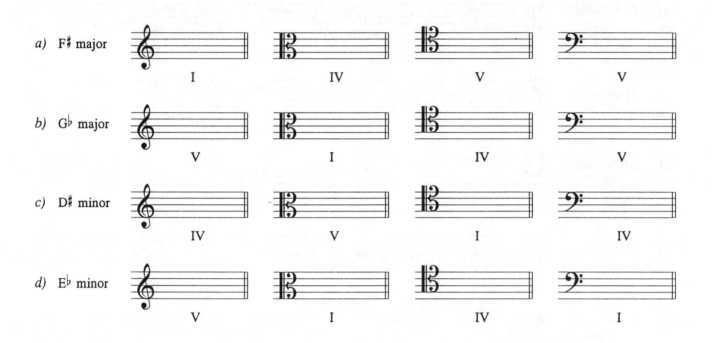

a) F# major   I   IV   V   V

b) G♭ major   V   I   IV   V

c) D# minor   IV   V   I   IV

d) E♭ minor   V   I   IV   I

F# major and G♭ major are enharmonic equivalents. That is, their scales sound the same although they are written differently:

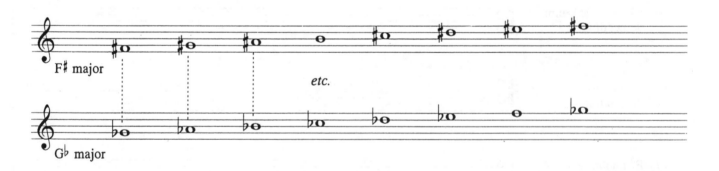

Likewise, D# minor and E♭ minor are also enharmonic equivalents:

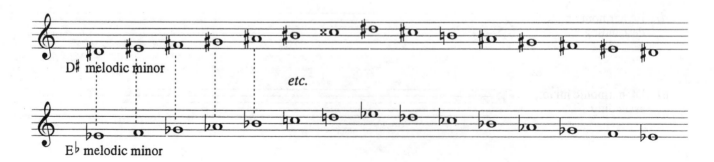

12

4. Name the key of each of the following scales. Without using any key signature, rewrite each of them in the enharmonic key. (An example has been shown.)

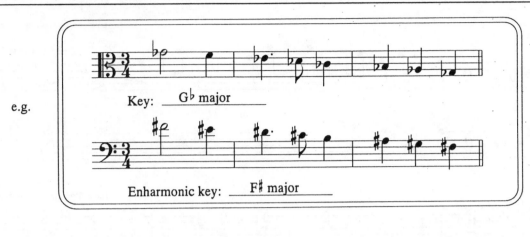

e.g.

Key: ___Gb major___

Enharmonic key: ___F# major___

a)

Key: _____

Enharmonic key: _____

b)

Key: _____

Enharmonic key: _____

c)

Key: _____

Enharmonic key: _____

d)

Key: _____

Enharmonic key: _____

5. Rewrite the following passages enharmonically (i.e. write keys with 6 flats using 6 sharps and vice versa.) Do not change the sound and remember to note the changes in the clefs. (The answer to the first opening has been shown.)

14

Supplementary Exercises

1. Add the correct clef and necessary accidentals to each of the following so as to form the scales named.

a) G♯ harmonic minor

b) B♭ major

c) C♯ melodic minor

d) F♯ major

e) F harmonic minor

f) E♭ major

g) B♭ harmonic minor

h) C melodic minor

i) E♭ melodic minor

j) G♯ melodic minor

k) D♯ harmonic minor

l) B major

15

2. Using the given rhythms, write each of the scales named. Complete the last bar with a rest or rests.

a)

B♭ melodic minor, ascending, with key signature. Start on the mediant.

b)

A♭ major, descending, without key signature. Begin on the dominant.

c)

F♯ harmonic minor, ascending, without key signature. Begin on the dominant.

d)

B major, ascending, with key signature. Begin on the subdominant.

e)

E♭ harmonic minor, descending, with key signature. Begin on the supertonic.

f)

D♯ melodic minor, descending, without key signature. Begin on the submediant.

3. Name the key of each of the following passages and then circle **any 3 notes within a bar** which would
form the tonic triad.

a)
Grieg, Sonata Op.45 No.3

Key: _____

b)
Faure, Elégie Op.24

Key: _____

c)
Bach, Prelude No.13 (from the '48' Bk I)

Key: _____

d)
Bach, Prelude (from the '48' Bk I)

Key: _____

e)
Haydn, Sonata

Key: _____

f)
Beethoven, Rasumowsky Quartet

Key: _____

g)
Moszkowski, Valse Mignonne

Key: _____

h)
Brahms, Intermezzo Op.117 No.2

Key: _____

i)
Brahms, Rhapsody Op.79

Key: _____

j)
Beethoven, Quartet Op.127

Key: _____

17

Transposition

In Grade 5, the student will be required to transpose a melody using any of the following intervals:

i)   Up or down an octave

ii) Up or down a major 2nd

iii) Up or down a minor 3rd

iv) Up or down a perfect 5th

Transposition up or down an octave

As covered in grade 3, the transposition of a melody involves moving the notes an octave higher or lower using only the treble and bass clefs. In Grade 5, the student must also be able to transpose a melody using the alto and tenor clefs. Always ensure that the melody is transposed by *one octave* only.

E.g.   Transpose this phrase down an octave using the alto and tenor clefs.

(You may work out the first note before writing the transposed melody in the other clefs.)

Thus:

1. Transpose each of these passages down an octave into the given clefs.

Brahms, Sonata in F minor

a)

b) Mozart, Cosi fan tutte

2. Transpose each of the passages up an octave into the given clefs.

a) Franck, Symphony in D minor

b) Berlioz, Romeo and Juliet

Transposition up or down a given interval

The Approach

1) Look at the key signature, then determine the key. Ignore the other accidentals. For example:

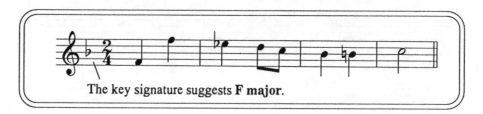

The key signature suggests **F major**.

2) The interval to which the melody is to be transposed will determine the new key. Thus:

Up a major 2nd, 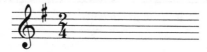 , the new key is G major. Write the new key signature:

The same approach is used for any other intervals.

3) Transpose the notes keeping them in their correct places, without regard for the accidentals, as required by the interval.

Thus, up a major 2nd:

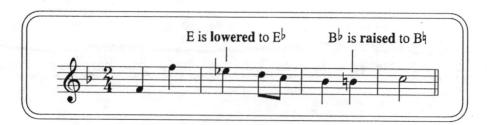

4) Look at the accidentals in the original melody again:

E is **lowered** to E♭   B♭ is **raised** to B♮

The notes are correspondingly raised or lowered, in the transposed version:

F♯ is **lowered** to F♮   C is **raised** to C♯

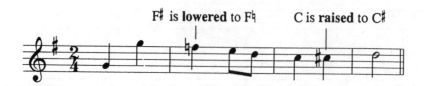

More examples:

Original melody

i)   Transposed up a minor 3rd   (, New key : A♭ major)

G ↘ G♭   D♭ ↗ D♮

ii) Transposed down a minor 3rd   (, New key : D major)

C♯ ↘ C♮   G ↗ G♯

iii) Transposed up a perfect 5th   (, New key : C major)

B ↘ B♭   F ↗ F♯

iv) Transposed down a perfect 5th   (, New key : B♭ major)

A ↘ A♭   E♭ ↗ E♮

Take note:

If a melody is written in the **minor** key or is regarded to be so, then the transposed melody must also be in the **minor** key.

For example:

This suggests the key of **E minor.**

Transposed up a major 2nd, , the new key is **F♯ minor.**

21

3. Transpose each of the following passages by the required interval. It should be useful for the student to indicate or assume the keys involved in the transposition. Every accidental requires a corresponding accidental in the transposed version. (The answer to the first opening has been shown.)

Up a major 2nd

a)

Bach, Fugue No.12 (from the '48' Bk I)

Assumed key: F minor

Transposed key: G minor

b)

Elgar, Falstaff Op.68

Assumed key: _____

Transposed key: _____

Down a major 2nd

c)

Liszt, Hungarian Rhapsody No.2

Assumed key: F♯ maj

Transposed key: E maj

d)

Prokofiev, Love for Three Oranges

Assumed key: C maj

Transposed key: B♭ maj

© Copyright 1922 by Hawkes & Son (London) Ltd.
Reprinted by permission of Boosey & Hawkes Music Publishers Ltd.

Up a minor 3rd

e)

Rameau, Suite in E minor, Tambourin

Assumed key: E min

Transposed key: G min

22

Down a minor 3rd

Up a perfect 5th

23

Down a perfect 5th

Brahms, Sextet Op.36

k)

Assumed key: _____

Transposed key: _____

Respighi, The Villa Medici Fountain
at Sunset

l)

Assumed key: _____

Transposed key: _____

4. Transpose the passage below by each of the required intervals.

Bruckner, Symphony No.8

etc.

a) Up a major 2nd

b) Down a minor 3rd

c) Down a perfect 5th

d) Up a perfect 5th

Transposing Instruments

Some instruments of the orchestra are transposing, that is they do not sound the notes as written but at some interval above or below.

Thus:

(i)   When an instrument in *B flat* plays middle C, it produces B♭, sounding **a major 2nd lower**.

Examples: Clarinet in B♭ and trumpet in B♭

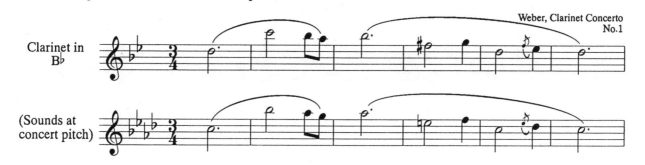

("Concert pitch" refers to the pitch at which the music is actually heard.)

(ii)   When an instrument *in A* plays middle C, the A below it is heard, sounding **a minor 3rd lower**.

Examples: Clarinet in A and cornet in A

(iii)   When an instrument *in F* plays middle C, the F below it is heard, sounding **a perfect 5th lower**.

Examples: Horn in F and cor anglais

Notice that for all of the above instruments, the concert pitch is always at an interval **lower**.

1. Write the following passages out at concert pitch. (The answer to the opening of the first exercise has been shown).

For Horn in F and Cor Anglais (i.e. sounding a perfect 5th lower)

a) Horn in F

Mozart, Concerto for Horn and Orchestra K417

p *con expressione*

b) Cor Anglais

Rimsky-Korsakov, Sniegourotchka

etc.

For Instruments in B♭ (i.e. sounding a major 2nd lower)

c) Trumpet in B♭

Edward Gregson, Prelude and Capriccio

d) Clarinet in B♭

Ferdinand David, Introduction, Theme and Variation

mf *con fuoco*

© Carl Fisher

For Instruments in A (i.e. sounding a minor 3rd lower)

e) Trumpet in A

Mozart, Clarinet Concerto K622

f) Clarinet in A

Bliss, Clarinet Quintet (1st movt)

mf *espressivo*

100% administered by BMG Music Publishing Singapore Pte Ltd obo Music Sales Group

26

2. Transpose the following passages, so that they will sound at concert pitch when played by the various instruments. Use key signatures, but add accidentals before all other notes which need them.

By Instruments in B♭ (i.e. a major 2nd higher)

Brahms, Sonata for Clarinet and Piano
in F minor Op. 120 No. 1

a)

Clarinet
in B♭

Scriabin, Prelude Op. 8 No. 1

b)

Cornet
in B♭

By Instruments in A (i.e. a minor 3rd higher)

Ravel, Le Tombeau de Couperin

c)

Clarinet
in A

Herbert Clarke, From the Shores of the
Mighty Pacific

d)

© Novello & Company Limited. Used by permission.

Trumpet
in A

By Instruments in F (i.e. a perfect 5th higher)

Franz Strauss, Concerto for
French Horn Op. 8

e)

Horn
in F

Debussy, La Mer (II)

f)

Cor
Anglais

3. Write each of the passages at concert pitch for the various instruments. Do not use key signatures but add any necessary accidentals.

a) Horn in F

Delius, Walk to the Paradise Garden

b) Clarinet in B♭

Rimsky-Korsakov, Servilia

c) Clarinet in A

Mendelssohn, The Hebrides

pp *tranquillo assai*

28

Intervals

In Grade 5, the intervals to be described may involve any two notes, including notes more than an octave apart. The lower note is not necessarily the key note. It would be useful to study the table below.

Interval		No. of Semitones
Major	2nd	2
Major	3rd	4
Perfect	4th	5
Perfect	5th	7
Major	6th	9
Major	7th	11
Perfect	8ve	12

An **augmented interval** is one semitone larger than a major or perfect interval. Thus an augmented 5th contains 8 semitones.

A **minor interval** is one semitone smaller than a major interval. Thus a minor 7th contains 10 semitones.

A **diminished interval** is one semitone smaller than a perfect interval but two semitones smaller than a major interval. Thus a diminished 7th has 9 semitones and a diminished 5th has 6 semitones.

1. Describe the following intervals fully.

e.g.

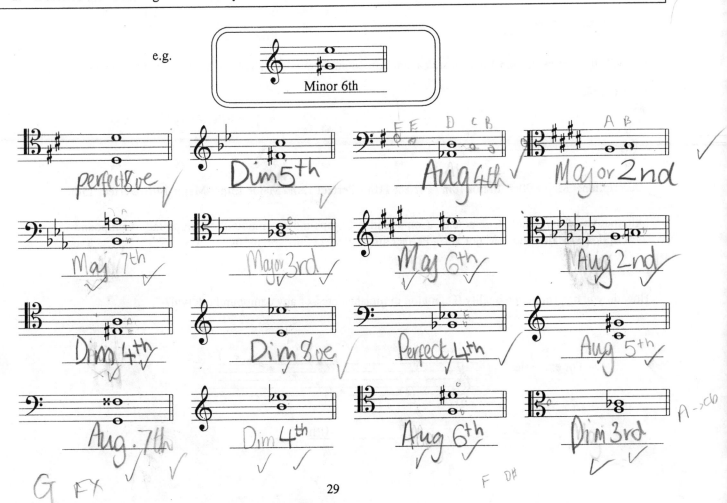

2. Write a note above each of the following notes so as to produce the given intervals.

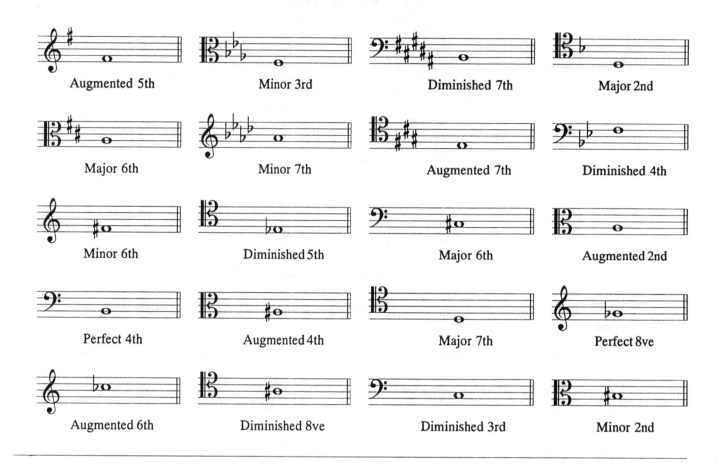

Augmented 5th	Minor 3rd	Diminished 7th	Major 2nd
Major 6th	Minor 7th	Augmented 7th	Diminished 4th
Minor 6th	Diminished 5th	Major 6th	Augmented 2nd
Perfect 4th	Augmented 4th	Major 7th	Perfect 8ve
Augmented 6th	Diminished 8ve	Diminished 3rd	Minor 2nd

Compound Intervals

Intervals that are more than 1 octave are called "compound intervals". They can be described in 2 ways.

For example:

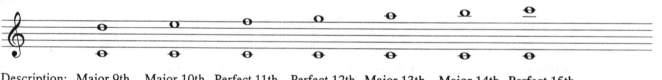

| Description: | Major 9th | Major 10th | Perfect 11th | Perfect 12th | Major 13th | Major 14th | Perfect 15th |
| Alternative description: | Compound Major 2nd | Compound Major 3rd | Compound Perfect 4th | Compound Perfect 5th | Compound Major 6th | Compound Major 7th | Compound Perfect 8ve |

How do you determine the quality (i.e. major, diminished etc.) of any compound interval?

For example:

?   10th

30

Approach:

Shift one of the notes an octave closer to the other.

Either  or

The interval is found to be an **augmented 3rd** (5 semitones).

Thus:

Augmented 10th (or compound augmented 3rd)

---

3. Describe fully each of the following compound intervals.

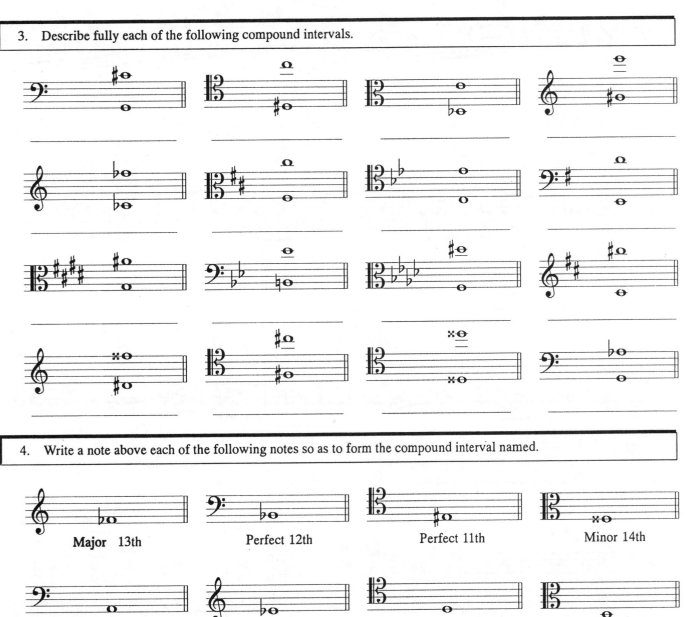

---

4. Write a note above each of the following notes so as to form the compound interval named.

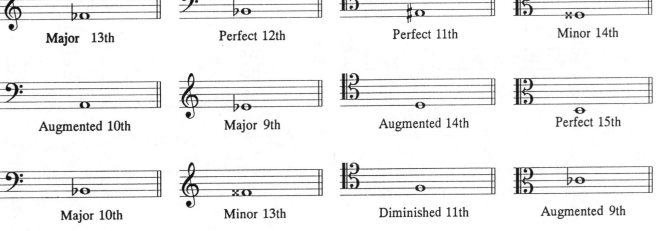

Major 13th	Perfect 12th	Perfect 11th	Minor 14th
Augmented 10th	Major 9th	Augmented 14th	Perfect 15th
Major 10th	Minor 13th	Diminished 11th	Augmented 9th

5. Describe fully each of the intervals marked ⌐‾‾⌐ in the following passages. Always calculate an interval from the lower note no matter which one comes first. (The first answer has been given).

a)
Mozart, Symphony No.1 (3rd movt)

1. ___Perfect 8ve___   3. _____

2. _____   4. _____

b)
Strauss, Salome Op.54

1. _____   3. _____

2. _____   4. _____

c)
Bloch, Concerto Grosso

1. _____   3. _____

2. _____   4. _____

d)
Bruckner, Quintet in F

1. _____   3. _____

2. _____   4. _____

e)
Copland, Piano Variations

1. _____   3. _____

2. _____   4. _____

6. In the passages below, describe the intervals at the points indicated by dotted lines.

Bach, 2 Part Invention No.15

1. _____   2. _____   3. _____

4. _____   5. _____   6. _____

7. _____   8. _____

Bach, French Suite No.2, Gigue

1. _____   2. _____   3. _____

4. _____   5. _____   6. _____

7. In the passage below, describe the intervals that are marked [ ] .

Beethoven, "Diabelli" Variations
No.30

1. _____   2. _____   3. _____

4. _____   5. _____   6. _____

7. _____   8. _____   9. _____

10. _____

Vocal Scores

Most vocal works are written for a combination of 4 voices: Soprano, Alto, Tenor and Bass (S. A. T. B.).
The music can be written either on short score (2 staves) or open score (4 staves).

Short Score

Note:

(i)   The treble stave is shared by Soprano (S) and Alto (A).

(ii)   The bass stave is shared by Tenor (T) and Bass (B).

(iii) Each stave has its separate bar-lines.

(iv)   The stems of the notes for (S) and (T) always go up, and those for (A) and (B) go down.

(v)   For two voices that share 1 stave, an accidental that occurs in 1 voice must be written
       in the other even if it occurs within the same bar. *

Open Score

The above passage can be transcribed into open score.

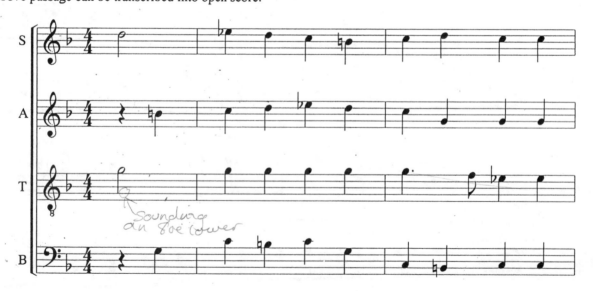

Note:

(i)   Each of the 4 voices is written on a separate stave with separate bar-lines.

(ii)   The tenor part is written an octave higher with a small 8 under the treble clef to show that it sounds
       an octave lower than written.

1. Transcribe each of the passages below into a short score. (The solution to the opening of the first example is given.)

a)

Boyce, I was glad

b)

Giovanni Croce, Is It Nothing To You?

35

c)

John Dryden, Ah fading joy, how quickly
art thou past!

d)

Phyllis Tate, Album Leaf

36

2. Transcribe the following passages into open score. (The answer to the first opening is given.)

a) Werlé, Spring and Fall

b) Elgar, The Shower

c)

Michael Burnett, Nowell Sing We Both
All and Some

d)

Gerard Schürmann, Summer is Coming

Identify Chords

In Grade V, the chords to be known are:

Tonic (I),   Supertonic (II),   Subdominant (IV)   and   Dominant (V)

For example:

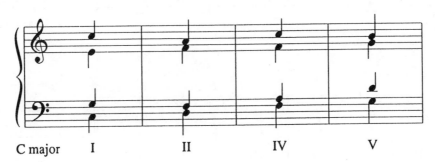

C major   I   II   IV   V

The student also needs to identify which position a chord is in, that is, whether the root, 3rd or 5th of the chord is in the bass.

For example, the tonic chord of C major may be written in 3 positions:

They may each be described as:	Tonic chord in root position (root in the bass)	Tonic chord in 1st inversion (3rd in the bass)	Tonic chord in 2nd inversion (5th in the bass)
The student may notate:	I or Ia	Ib	Ic
An alternative notation (figured bass):	$I\frac{5}{3}$	$I\frac{6}{3}$	$I\frac{6}{4}$

In the exercises to follow, the student may indicate his chords by using any of the following acceptable notations:

1) Roman numerals   i.e.   I, II, IV, V

2) Notations used in jazz and popular music   e.g. Dm, Gm

3) Figured bass   e.g.   [figured bass example: two notes in bass clef marked 6 and $\frac{5}{3}$]

4) Write out the notes in full on the staves.

1. Name the key of each of the passages and then identify the numbered chords.

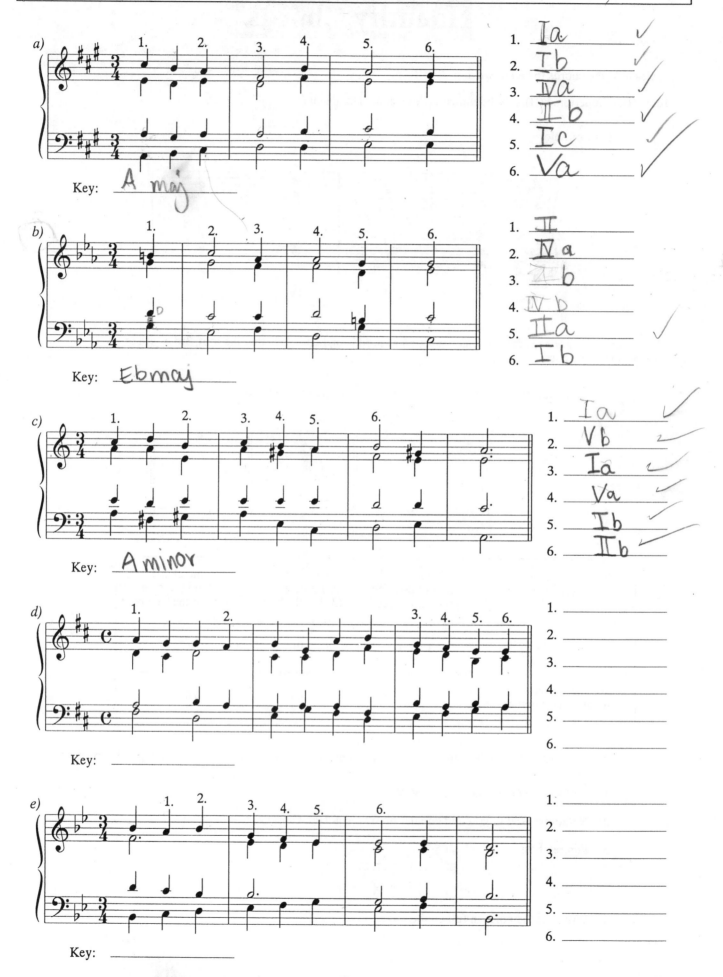

a)

Key: __A maj__

1. Ia ✓
2. Ib ✓
3. IVa ✓
4. IIb ✓
5. Ic ✓
6. Va ✓

b)

Key: __Ebmaj__

1. II
2. IVa
3. Ib
4. IVb
5. IIa ✓
6. Ib

c)

Key: __A minor__

1. Ia ✓
2. Vb ✓
3. Ia ✓
4. Va ✓
5. Ib ✓
6. IIb ✓

d)

Key: _____

1. _____
2. _____
3. _____
4. _____
5. _____
6. _____

e)

Key: _____

1. _____
2. _____
3. _____
4. _____
5. _____
6. _____

40

2. Identify the key and the chords marked * in each of the following passages.

Eric Thiman, O, No John

a)

Key: _____ _____ _____ _____ _____

Mendelssohn

b)

Key: _____ _____ _____ _____ _____

c)

J.S. Bach, Chorale "Allein Gott
in der Hoh' sei Ehr"

Key: _____ _____ _____ _____ _____

Beethoven, Piano Sonata Op.10

d)

Key: _____ _____ _____

J.S. Bach, Chorale "Sollt' ich meinem Gott
nicht elugen"

e)

Key: _____ _____ _____ _____

41

f) Schumann, Piano Concerto in A minor

Key: _____ _____

g) Verdi

Key: _____ _____

h) Chopin, Prelude Op.28

Key: _____ _____ _____

i) Beethoven, "Appassionata" (2nd movt)

Key: _____ _____ _____

j) Bach, Chorale Cantata 88

Key: _____ _____ _____ _____

42

Cadences

Cadences normally occur at the end of phrases. Each cadence consists of 2 chords. In Grade 5, only the chords I, II, IV and V (all in root position) will be used.

The cadences to be known are:
(All examples are in C major)

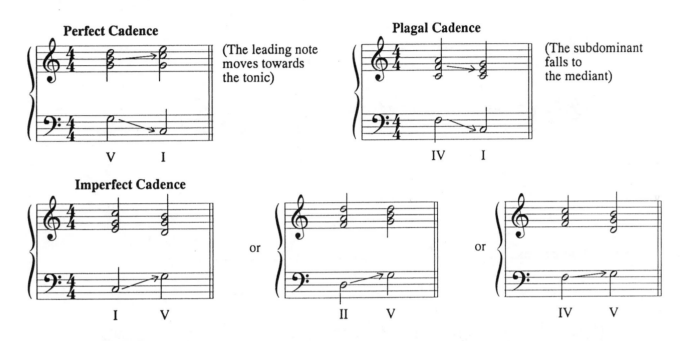

1. In each of the following, choose suitable chords to form cadences. Name the cadence in each case. (A working stave has been provided.) Only the keys of C, G, D and F majors are used.

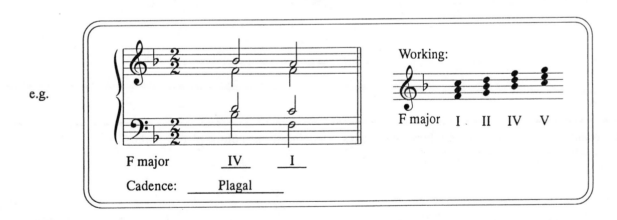

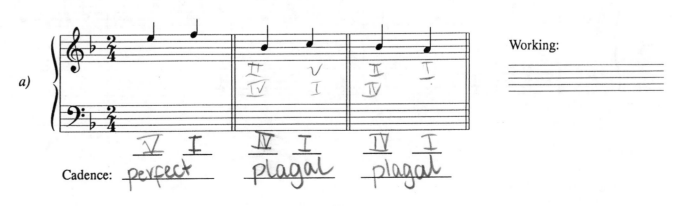

b)

C maj

Working:

Cadence: perfect   perfect   plagal

c)

Working:

Cadence: _____   _____   _____

d)

Working:

Cadence: _____   _____   _____

2. Name the key of each of the following passages. Underneath each of the places marked ⌈ * * ⌉ choose 2 suitable chords to form cadences.

a)

Key: _____   _____   _____   _____   _____

44

b)

Key: _____ ___ ___ ___ ___ ___

c)

Key: _____ ___ ___ ___ ___ ___ ___

d)

Key: _____ ___ ___ ___ ___ ___

e)

Key: _____ ___ ___ ___ ___ ___

In harmonising a melody, take note that:

i)   A long note may be harmonised by 2 chords:

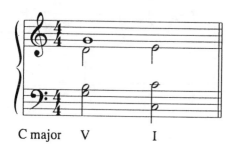

C major   V   I

ii) A chord may be used to harmonise more than 1 note:

etc.

F major   I   V

iii) Passing notes and auxillary notes are not to be harmonised:

Passing Note:

etc.

G major   V   I

A *passing note* lies between
2 harmony notes on either side,
one above and one below it.

Auxillary Note:

C major   V   I

An *auxillary note* occurs between
the repetition of a harmony note.
The harmony note may be a step
above or below.

46

3. In each of the following passages, choose suitable chords for the places marked 1.⌐———⌐ 2.⌐———⌐ etc. If you choose to fill in the notes, remember to consider the time value of the chords to be held.

Traditional, "Jingle Bells"

a)

Traditional, "Peas Porridge Hot"

b)

Cavalli

c)

Traditional, Ye Banks and Braes

d)

e)

f)

g)

h)

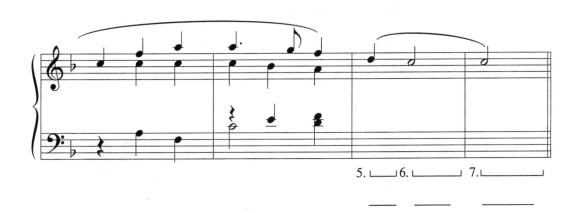

Composing a Melody

In Grade 5, the student will be required to compose a melody of not more than 8 bars either for an instrument or for voice. When writing for an instrument, take note of the following points:

i)   Specify the instrument of your choice.

ii)   Bear in mind the range of each particular instrument and its characteristics.
         For example, string instruments may play pizzicato notes. Instruments such as the cello, horn and trombone usually play slow moving passages.

iii)   Choose the correct clef appropriate for the instrument. For example, the viola may use the alto clef and the trombone may use the tenor clef.

How to compose a good melody

The Rhythmic Structure

i)   Write an 8-bar rhythm divided into 2 halves, each ending with a relatively long note.
         Remember, the given bars are to be counted.

ii)   Make use of repetitions where appropriate. (See Grades 2 and 3 on "Four bar rhythms"):

e.g.

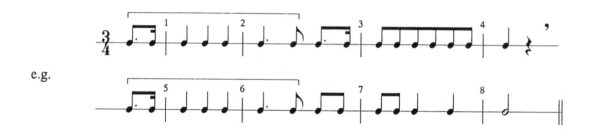

Notice in the above, *the opening of the 1st half is repeated in that of the 2nd half.*

The Melodic Structure

The student may consider the following points to construct the melody.

i)   Exact repetition

         Where an opening rhythm repeats itself, the same notes may also be repeated:

Brahms, Symphony No.4

e.g.

ii)   Modified Repetition

To avoid boredom, the repetition may be slightly modified; that is, to repeat the same
rhythm using different notes:

e.g.

A rhythmic repetition may also occur with the notes at a degree higher or lower:

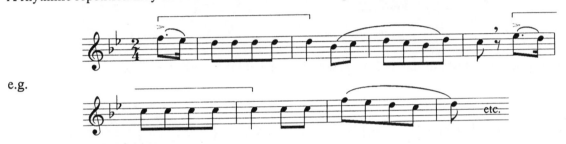

e.g.

iii)   Sequence

A melodic figure may be repeated immediately with all the notes moving up (or down) by 1 degree:

e.g.

iv)   Movement of notes

a)   The melody should have a sense of direction or shape. It may move towards
a high point (a climax) and then down again. Avoid moving aimlessly around
the same few notes.

b)   Use scalic movement at most times. Leaps are good for contrasts; but avoid too many of
them, otherwise the melody may lose its shape.

c)   Avoid dissonant intervals such as the augmented 2nd and the augmented 4th as they make
unmusical movement:

The diminished 5th interval may be used but it should resolve melodically within its compass:

d)   When writing in a minor key, it is advisable to use the melodic form.

Cadences

End the first half of the melody on an imperfect cadence i.e. on a note of the dominant chord (V).
The final note should be the tonic itself:

Do not leap abruptly towards the end. You may adopt one of the following endings:

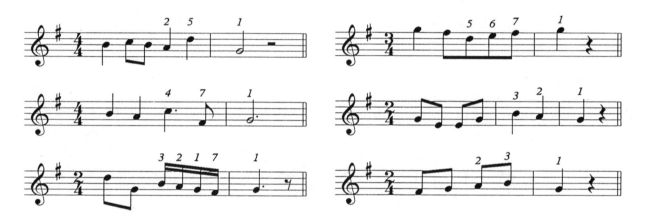

(The numbers correspond to the movable solfege system.)

Final points

Include all performance directions:

i)   Phrases, slurs and articulation marks (e.g. staccato marks, bow marks.)

ii)   Tempo direction (e.g. Allegro, Andante, ♩ = *100*)

iii)   Dynamics (e.g. *p* , *f* , *cresc*, *dim.*)

1. Compose a melody of not more than 8 bars using each of the openings. Choose one of the instruments named. Indicate whether a chosen transposing instrument is at transposed pitch or at concert pitch. You may change the clef if necessary. All performance directions should be included.

Choice of instrument: _____

a) for violin, trumpet or clarinet.

Choice of instrument: _____

b) for oboe, horn or clarinet.

Choice of instrument: _____

c) for cello, bassoon or trombone.

Choice of instrument: _____

d) for violin, clarinet or trumpet.

e)   Choice of instrument: _____

for violin, clarinet
or trumpet.

f)   Choice of instrument: _____

for cello, bassoon
or trombone.

g)   Choice of instrument: _____

for violin, clarinet
or flute.

h)   Choice of instrument: _____

for viola, oboe
or horn.

i)   Choice of instrument: _____

for cello, bassoon
or trombone.

j)   Choice of instrument: _____

for violin, flute
or trumpet.

k)   Choice of instrument: _____

for oboe, horn
or clarinet.

l)   Choice of instrument: _____

for cello, bassoon
or trombone.

Setting a Melody to Words

The basic principles of melodic writing outlined in the previous chapter apply likewise in setting words to music. However, there are a few differences.

i)   The opening bars are not given.

ii)   Voices have smaller ranges compared to instruments, therefore it would be advisable to write within this range:

iii)   Wide leaps are to be avoided as they are unsuitable for singers.

iv)   The rhythm should be kept simple with at least one note to a syllable. The tempo marking chosen must also be appropriate. For example, *presto* is too fast to be sung.

Consider the words when writing for the voice, which in themselves suggest musical ideas such as the rhythm, the mood and melodic shape.

The Rhythm and the Mood

In setting words to music, the rhythm is determined by the natural speech rhythm.

For example:

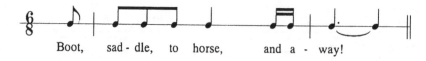

The melody should also suggest the mood of the words. For example, "happy words" should be written in a major key and "sad words" suggest the use of a minor key in slow-moving rhythms.

For example:

The Structure

In writing the melody, some sort of plan is needed to achieve a sense of unity. It is a common practice to divide the verse into 2 equal halves, each containing 2 phrases. The use of rhythmic repetition is recommended. (See Grade 3: Simple Phrase Structure.)

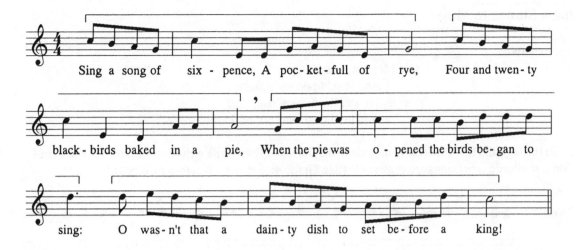

In the above example, the opening rhythm ♩♩♩♩ | ♩ is repeated at the beginning of the 2nd and 3rd phrases.

However, if certain phrases or words are repeated, the student may repeat only that portion of the melody.

For example:

The Melodic Shape

A melody must have a shape, i.e. it should have a sense of direction. Certain words in the poem may suggest a high point i.e. a climax in the melody. Such a climax should be given both length and height within the melodic curve.

For example:

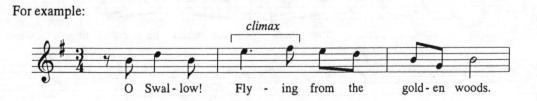

Setting a Stanza to Music

For example:

Old Meg she was a Gipsy,
And lived upon the moors:
Her bed it was the brown heath turf,
And her house was out of doors.

1) Read through the lines, marking the accented syllables. Then write a rhythm suitable for the words. Some rhythmic repetitions are preferred. (See Grade 4: Setting a Rhythm to Words.)

2) Fill in the melody; meanwhile bear in mind the following:

   i) A cadence must occur at the end of each phrase.

   ii) Repetitions or sequences may be used to achieve unity.

   iii) The climax of the words usually (though not always) occurs at the 3rd line.

   iv) Sing the melody as you write. Avoid writing a melody that is pointlessly complicated.

This setting is "syllabic": i.e. each syllable has one note. Of course, syllables may be set to 2 or more notes. Here is an example.

58

1. Compose melodies to the following words. Write each syllable clearly under the note or notes to which it is to be sung. Indicate the speed, dynamics and other necessary performance directions.

a)   Sweet day, so cool, so calm, so bright
      The bridal of the earth and sky —

George Herbert

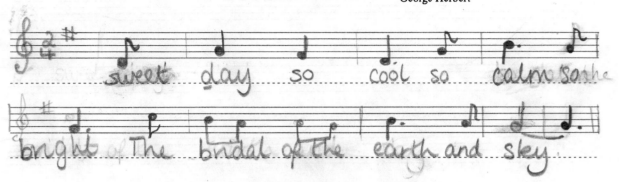

sweet day so cool so calm so the
bright of The bridal of the earth and sky

b)   A Maid whom there were none to praise
      And very few to love.
      A violet by a mossy stone
      Half hidden from the eye!

William Wordsworth

c)   Her cheeks were like the cherry
      Her skin was white as snow;
      When she was blithe and merry
      She angel-like did show.

George Wither

d)   The moon is behind, and at the full
And yet she looks both small and dull.
The night is chill, the cloud is gray:
'Tis a month before the month of May.

John Keats

e)   With blackest moss the flower-pots
Were thickly crusted, one and all:
The rusted nails fell from the knots
That held the pear to the garden-wall.

Lord Tennyson

f)   Alone, alone, all all alone,
Alone on a wide wide sea!
And never a saint took pity on
My soul in agony.

S.T. Coleridge

g)   I bring fresh showers for the thirsting flowers
          From the seas and streams,
          I bear light shade for the leaves when laid
          In their noonday dreams.

Percy Bysshe Shelley

h)   Sweet was the sound, when oft at evening's close
          Up yonder hill the village murmur rose.

Oliver Goldsmith

i)   The streams thro' many a lilied row
          Down-carolling to the crisped sea,
          Low-tinkled with a bell-like flow
             Atween the blossoms, 'We are free'.

Tennyson

j)   When the voices of children are heard on the green,
And laughing is heard on the hill,
My heart is at rest within my breast,
And everything else is still.

Anonymous

k)   And then the whining school-boy, with his satchel,
And shining morning face, creeping like snail
Unwillingly to school.

William Shakespeare

l)   A land of streams! Some, like a downward smoke,
Slow-dropping veils of thinnest lawn, did go.

Lord Tennyson

Ornaments

---

1. Name the ornament sign used in each of the following.

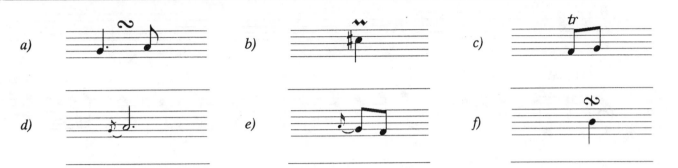

---

2. Copy out the melody, replacing the notes under each of the brackets ⌐‾‾‾¬ with the appropriate ornament sign.

Musical Terms and Signs

Italian Terms

Apart from the terms studied in the previous grades, the following Italian terms are to be known.
Explain them.

1. On Tempo

    doppio movimento _____

    incalzando _____

    tosto _____

    volante _____

2. On Performance Direction

    attacca _____

    loco _____

    lunga pausa _____

    rinforzando, rf, rfs _____

    segue _____

    pochettino (poch.) _____

3. On Expression / Style

    dolente _____

    dolore _____

    doloroso _____

    estinto _____

    lacrimoso _____

    lusingando _____

    piacevole _____

    smorzando (smorz.) _____

    teneramente _____

    tenerezza _____

4.   <u>Other Terms</u>

   misura   _____

           e.g.   *alla misura:*   _____

                  senza misura: _____

German Terms

Explain the following German terms:

1.   <u>On Tempo</u>

   langsam   _____

   mässig   _____

   schnell   _____

2.   <u>On Performance style / expression</u>

   Ausdruck   _____

   Ausdrucksvoll   _____

   bewegt   _____

   breit   _____

   einfach   _____

   fröhlich   _____

   lebhaft   _____

   ruhig   _____

   süss   _____

   traurig   _____

   zart   _____

3.   <u>Other Terms</u>

   aber   _____

   ein   _____

   etwas   _____

           (e.g.   *etwas traurig:*   _____   )

immer _____

(e.g.   *immer lebhafter:* _____)

mit _____

(e.g.   *mit ped.:* _____)

nicht _____

(e.g.   *nicht zu langsam:* _____)

ohne _____

(e.g.   *ohne ped:* _____)

Rest and Repetitions

1. Explain the following signs for rests.

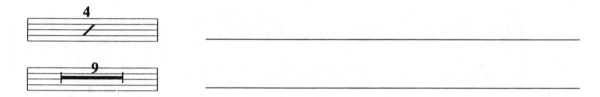

_____

_____

2. Write out in full how each of the following should be played.

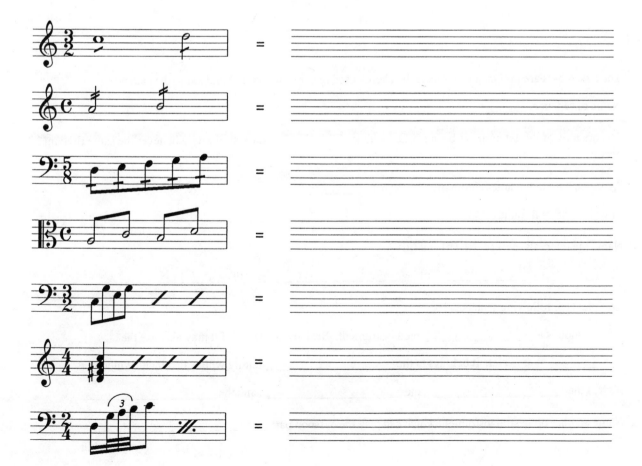

General Exercises

1. This is the Adagio for Two Horns and Bassoon K410 by Mozart. Look at it, and then answer the questions that follow.

a) The first 4 bars are in F major. Indicate the chords used in bar 4 (marked *) and name the cadence.

   Name of cadence: _____

b) The opening of the 1st horn has been marked with a ⌐￣￣￢ . Mark similarly whenever the same rhythm occurs.

c) At which bar are the notes chromatic?   At bar _____

   In which part is it found?   _____

d) Name the intervals marked (i), (ii) and (iii).

   (i) _____   (ii) _____   (iii) _____

e) Complete the following sentences.

   The bassoon is a _____ reed instrument. Besides the bass clef it may also use the

   _____ clef. It belongs to the _____ family which also include members

   such as the _____, the _____, and the _____.

f) Name another orchestral instrument which can play the bassoon part. _____.

g)   Name another orchestral instrument which transposes at the same interval as Horn in F.

_____

h)   As printed above, the horns are at concert pitch. Transpose the 1st horn part up a perfect 5th, to show the notation required by the player.

2.   This passage is from Rimsky-Korsakov's Opera *The Tsar's Bride*. Look at it and then answer the questions below.

a)   Which 4 instruments are playing the extract?

_____

b)   To which family do the instruments belong? _____

Name 3 other instruments of the same family. _____, _____

and _____.

c)   Why do the 2 staves use different key-signatures?

_____

d)   Rewrite bars 5 to 8 in open score, with the clarinet parts at concert pitch, i.e. transposed down a major 2nd.

e)   Assume that the key is F major. Use the open score of the above question to describe the chords marked (i), (ii) in bar 5 and (iii) in bar 6.

(i) _____   (ii) _____   (iii) _____

f)   Describe the intervals marked ⟩ x and ⟩ y in bars 2 and 7.

⟩ x _____   ⟩ y _____

g)   Name the ornament sign found at bar 8.

_____

h)   Explain the following terms:

Allegretto   _____

♩ = **112**   _____

dim.   _____

mf   _____

3. This passage is a reduction from the 2nd movement of Haydn's Trumpet Concerto in E♭.
   Look at it and then answer the questions that follow.

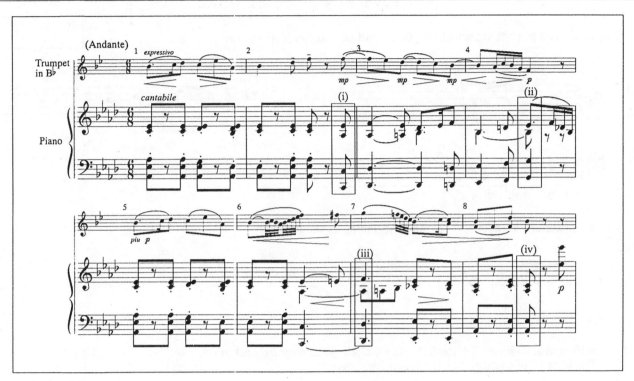

a)   Name the key of this passage.   _____

      Which other key may have the same key-signature?   _____

b)   Give the meaning of the following terms:

      Andante   _____

      expressivo   _____

      cantabile   _____

      piu p   _____

c)   Choose a suitable speed from the following and then write it at the appropriate place.

      ♩ = 40   ♩. = 100   ♪ = 80   ♪ = 176

d)   Complete the sentences:

      The trumpet belongs to the _____ family. At concert pitch, trumpet in B♭ sounds

      _____ lower than written. Three other transposing instruments of the orchestra are

      the _____, the _____ and the _____.

e)   What can you say about the melody at bars 5 and 6 as compared to bars 1 and 2?

      _____

f)   Describe the chords marked ☐ in bars 2, 4, 7 and 8.

      (i)   _____   (ii)   _____

      (iii)   _____   (iv)   _____

Specimen Test

1. a) Add a rest or rests at each of the places marked * to complete the bar.

   b) Write a four-bar rhythm in $\frac{7}{8}$ time, beginning as shown.

2. Write out at concert pitch the following melody written for trumpet in B♭.
   The interval of transposition is a major 2nd lower.

Georges Hüe, Contest Pieb

poco ad lib.   *accel.*   *rall. e dim.*

3. a) Give the full name of this scale.

Scale _____

   b) Rewrite the above at an octave lower using the tenor clef. Use the key signature and add any essential accidentals.

4. a) Write the key signature of the keys named below.

   C# minor   E♭ minor   B major

72

b) Describe fully each of the intervals and also name a key in which each may be found.

Interval _____

Key _____

Interval _____

Key _____

5. a) Describe each chord marked * as I, II, IV or V. Also indicate their positions
   i.e. whether the root, third or fifth is in the bass.

   | 15 |

   b) Underneath the last 2 notes, write a suitable chord for each. You may use I, II, IV or V
   or any recognised method of notation.

6. EITHER

   | 15 |

   a) Write a melody for violin or flute using the given opening. Add marks of
      tempo, expression and other performance directions suitable for the instrument
      chosen. The melody should not be more than 8 bars.

                                             Choice of instrument: _____

   OR

   b) Compose a melody for the following words. Write each syllable under the note or notes to which it is to be sung.

                    In the earth - thou shalt be laid,
                    A stone standing over thee.

                              Emily Bronte

73

7. This extract is from the Notturno of Borodin's String Quartet No.2. Look at it and then answer the questions below.

a) (i) Give the meaning of the following:

Andante _____

pp dolce _____

cant. col espress. _____

fp _____

(ii) Name the ornament used in bar 2. _____

b) (i) The passage is written for a string quartet. Write the correct names of the instruments used, before the staves of this extract.

(ii) How can the instrument on the 3rd stave play two notes at the same time? Name the term used.

_____

(iii) What do the terms 'pizzicato' and 'arco' mean in string music?

_____

c) (i) Describe the intervals marked x⌈ , y⌈ and z⌈ in bars 2, 5 and 6.

(x) _____ (y)_____ (z)_____

(ii) Using the tenor clef, transpose the bass part of bars 1 to 3 an octave lower. Include the key signature, time signature and dynamics.

_____

74